Informal Assessments for
Vocabulary Development

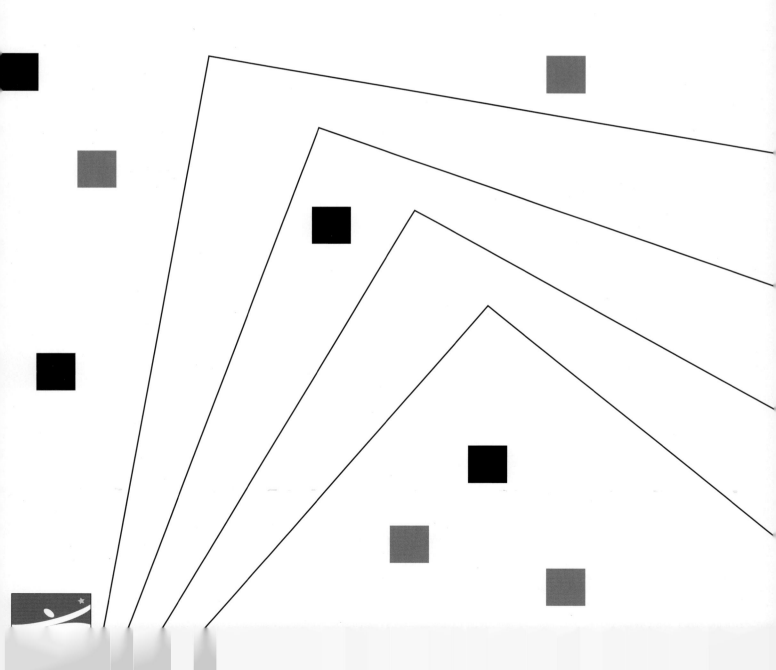

Benchmark Education Company
629 Fifth Avenue • Pelham, NY 10803
www.benchmarkeducation.com

ISBN: 978-1-4509-2884-7

For ordering information, call Toll-Free 1-877-236-2465 or visit our Web site: www.benchmarkeducation.com.

Informal Assessments for Vocabulary Development

Table of Contents

Assessment Introduction

Daily teaching goes hand in hand with ongoing assessment and evaluation. The wide variety of reading, writing, spelling, and language assessments provided by Benchmark Education Company enables teachers to:

- obtain multiple perspectives on the literacy growth occurring in their classrooms;
- monitor and reflect on their teaching and students' learning;
- make informed decisions about students' progress and needs;
- select appropriate materials and instructional techniques that match students' current level of development;
- document progress over time through a cumulative portfolio;
- report progress to students, parents, and administrators.

Meaningful, ongoing, and multifaceted observation is the heart of the evaluation process. Since observations must occur in authentic contexts, utilize your small-group reading time to document students' efforts to join discussions; ask and answer questions; react to prompts; contribute ideas for graphic organizers; process texts; problem-solve new words; apply targeted skills and strategies, and act out and/or talk, draw, or write about books.

The integration of assessment, teaching, and learning supports effective literacy instruction. Benchmark Education Company provides teachers with the tools for understanding and documenting literacy development. Teachers can use this information to differentiate instruction by developmental reading behaviors and characteristics, metacognitive and comprehension strategy needs, instructional reading levels, fluency, and vocabulary understandings.

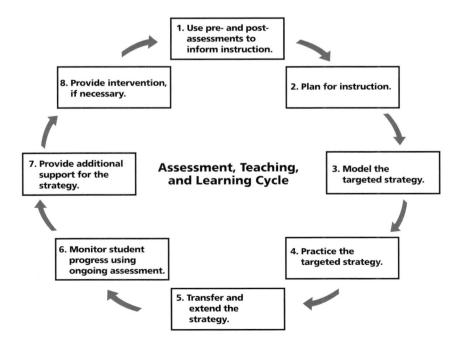

Assessment, Teaching, and Learning Cycle

1. Use pre- and post-assessments to inform instruction.
2. Plan for instruction.
3. Model the targeted strategy.
4. Practice the targeted strategy.
5. Transfer and extend the strategy.
6. Monitor student progress using ongoing assessment.
7. Provide additional support for the strategy.
8. Provide intervention, if necessary.

Rhodes and Shanklin (1993) outline the eleven principles of literacy assessment. Each of these principles is supported in every Benchmark Education Company assessment product.

11 Principles of Literacy Assessment	How BEC Assessment Tools Support the Principles
1. Assess authentic reading and writing.	A variety of ongoing informal assessment tools are available for use before, during, and after literacy instruction.
2. Assess reading and writing in a variety of contexts.	Assessment tools can be administered one-on-one, in small groups, or with the whole class.
3. Assess the literacy environment, instruction, and students.	Assessment tools prompt teacher reflection and provide direction on linking assessment results to instruction.
4. Assess processes as well as products.	Rubrics and assessment tools are available for lesson analysis and noting observable developmental behaviors and characteristics.
5. Analyze error patterns in reading and writing.	Oral reading records and rubrics identify error patterns, strengths, and needs.
6. Consider background knowledge in the assessment of reading and writing.	Student interest questionnaires and surveys gain insight into a students' literacy background and understandings.
7. Base assessment on normal developmental patterns and behavior in reading and writing.	A variety of reading behaviors and characteristics checklists are available to assist in noting developmental milestones and then reporting and planning during assessment meetings.
8. Clarify and use standards in the assessment of reading and writing.	Assessments are aligned with National Literacy Standards and state expectations for learning.
9. Use triangulation to corroborate data and make decisions.	Multiple assessments target different areas of literacy development and are designed to facilitate triangulation of data.
10. Involve students, parents, and other school personnel in the assessment process.	Sharing results from the Benchmark Education Assessments in data team meetings and parent conferences informs and involves others in the process of linking assessment and instruction.
11. Make assessment an ongoing part of everyday reading and writing opportunities and instruction.	Each assessment book provides guidance on how to schedule, manage, organize, and store assessments. Calendars and other planning tools are also provided.

Benchmark Education Company Assessment

The Benchmark Education Company Assessment resources provide tools for ongoing literacy assessments. Each resource has a variety of planning and assessment tools that can be used to inform instruction. Assessment resources can be administered to the whole group, small group, or individual students.

Informal Assessments for Reading Development

- tools for documenting reading behaviors over time, acquisition of concepts about print, and English-language development
- oral reading records
- prompting guides
- reading conference note-taking forms that focus on characteristics of reading development

Informal Assessments for Text Comprehension

- tools for assessing metacognitive and comprehension strategy understandings
- tools for genre and text structure retellings
- comprehension prompting guides
- reading conference note-taking forms that focus on comprehension strategy development

Informal Assessments for Fluency Development

- tools for assessing accuracy, rate, prosody, and oral reading performances
- prompting guides
- reading conference note-taking forms that focus on fluency development

Informal Assessments for Vocabulary Development

- tools for assessing Tier One, Two, and Three vocabulary understandings
- prompting guides
- reading conference note-taking forms that focus on vocabulary development

Informal Assessments for Writing Development

- tools for assessing writing development
- rubric and checklists for assessing genre and text structure
- writing conference note-taking forms

Scheduling, Managing, Organizing, and Storing Assessments

Documenting progress through a cumulative portfolio is one of the greatest advantages of classroom-based assessment. Following are some tips to carry out this process in a teacher- and student-friendly manner.

Scheduling Assessments

Use some assessments as pre- and post-evaluations of growth and development, completing them at the beginning and end of the school year. Conduct other assessments on a more frequent basis as needed. Assess informally during literacy activities every day. Schedule an individual literacy conference with each student every month, and use the information in instructional planning. Hold additional reading and writing conferences as needed to meet students' immediate needs, allowing students to schedule conferences with you as well. Assess students in greatest need of intervention or additional instructional support more frequently—every one to two weeks.

Planning Calendars

Planning calendars help teachers schedule and manage assessments throughout the school year. Teachers can use the masters in the Appendix to note key dates for administering and gathering assessment data for an entire class or individual students.

Year-at-a-Glance Planning Calendar Record state, district, and classroom scheduled assessment dates. (See Appendix page 76)

Month-at-a-Glance Planning Calendar Record progress-monitoring assessments for the entire class or 1–3 students per day. (See Appendix page 77)

Week-at-a-Glance Planning Calendar Record progress-monitoring assessments and individual reading conferences for the week. (See Appendix page 78)

Managing Assessments

Start with one assessment tool and gradually build to the desired collection, as indicated in the following implementation steps.

1. Organize your classroom learning environment. Establish consistent routines and clear expectations for a variety of instructional settings, including whole-group, small-group, and independent activities.
2. Create a management system and schedule for administering formal and informal assessment measures. Identify a simple storage and retrieval system. Set a manageable schedule.
3. Start slowly and proceed one student at a time until all are assessed and you have identified their literacy developmental stages, strengths, and needs.
4. Create class profiles of your findings to serve as a lesson-planning reference and cumulative documentation of growth. Update the profile with each month's individual student conference data.
5. Reflect on the information gathered:

    Are students progressing in a timely fashion?

    What is their overall growth during a specified time frame?

    Are your goals for students being met?

    Is your assessment informing instruction and vice versa?

    Do you see transfer of the skills, strategies, and behaviors you have modeled and taught?

    Do the students in your class reflect the national standards and expectations for their grade level?

Organizing and Storing Assessment Materials

A simple plan for collecting and retrieving each type of record will ensure success and ongoing implementation.

Color code and use separate pocket folders or three-ring binders for each aspect of literacy to be assessed. Have a clearly identified and labeled location to house the individual student assessment folders or binders. Within each folder or binder, use dividers and pockets to store the completed individual assessment tools and work samples.

Store the completed group profile charts in lesson-planning books or create a separate three-ring binder. The binder can serve as an instructional reference tool and cumulative documentation of teaching and learning. Use index tab dividers to note the different profile charts to be collected and used over a school year. Include national, state, and district grade-level recommendations and expectations to complete this instructional reference binder.

Observations and Responsive Teaching

Daily observations of students engaged in meaningful literacy experiences provide detailed information regarding literacy development, strengths and needs. Documenting observations on a regular basis provides opportunities for teachers to reflect on instruction and areas in need of further assessment. As Tomlinson & McTighe (2006) remind us, "Responsive teaching suggests a teacher will make modifications in how students get access to important ideas and skills, in ways that students make sense of and demonstrate essential ideas and skills, and in the learning environment—all with an eye to supporting maximum success for each learner." Observations of student learning and transfer provide the link between the assessment and instruction process.

Anecdotal Notes

Anecdotal notes are the observations that are written by the teacher during or after a literacy event. These detailed notes capture students' processing behaviors so they may be further analyzed and used to inform the next instructional move. Anecdotal notes can be taken in whole- or small-group settings or for individuals. These informal notes contain valuable information about students' strengths, weaknesses, progress, needs, processing abilities, or any other observations teachers feel are significant.

Use the Anecdotal Notes master (Appendix page 79) to record notes and observations. Place one small sticky note in each box (one per student). After recording the student's name, date, and your observations, transfer the sticky notes to individual students' portfolios.

What Research Says About Vocabulary Development

Vocabulary growth occurs naturally when students read, write, talk, and listen to one another on a daily basis. Listening and speaking vocabularies traditionally develop as young children begin to acquire language. Reading and writing vocabularies often develop in more formal, academic settings as students gain greater control of their listening and speaking vocabularies. The end result is often a reading vocabulary that outmatches any of the other vocabulary components. Listening, speaking, reading, and writing vocabularies all grow when encouraged in a rich literary environment, such as a classroom. Students internalize the language used in meaningful contexts and expand their word knowledge.

As outlined in the report on the National Reading Panel (2000), vocabulary should:

- be taught both directly and indirectly,
- be a part of reading instruction, and
- involve the active engagement of learners in specific tasks.

Indirect vocabulary knowledge stems from students' ability to grasp or pick up the meaning of many words through the daily exposure to oral and written communications. Discussing concepts and real world issues, listening to texts that are read aloud, and reading texts independently help students build indirect vocabulary. In her book *Words, Words, Words*, Janet Allen (1999) states, "They used the words they heard on television and radio; they used words from the music they listened to; and they used the words I used with them." Vocabulary growth occurs naturally when students read, write, talk, and listen to one another on a daily basis. When surrounded with a rich literary environment, students internalize the language used in the classroom in meaningful contexts.

Janet Allen suggests questions to help drive instruction for the different types of word knowledge. These questions help determine which words require pre-teaching and prior knowledge, which can be taught on the spot, and which can be defined from the text.

Which words are most important to understanding the text?

How much prior knowledge will students need to have about this word or its related concept?

Is the word encountered frequently?

Does the word have multiple meanings?

Which words can be figured out from context?

What strategies could I employ to help students integrate the concept into their lives?

How can I help students use the word or concept in meaningful ways in multiple contexts?

Direct vocabulary instruction occurs when a teacher systematically demonstrates how to determine the meanings of words by utilizing contextual and conceptual clues. Although students learn the words in the context of authentic reading, the teacher leads them to specific strategies for discovering meaning. Research indicates that direct vocabulary instruction is necessary to ensure that students grow as readers and thinkers in both fiction and content-area literacy. Direct vocabulary instruction nurtures an understanding of new concepts, enhances the craft of writing, develops a deeper understanding of the words and concepts students are partially aware of, increases reading comprehension, and improves communication skills (Allen, 1999).

Direct vocabulary knowledge is the outgrowth of explicit instruction on words that may be unfamiliar or challenging. Direct instruction should provide students with word-study and word-solving strategies to help them build their vocabularies. While context clues help students with basic information about words, teachers must directly teach the meanings of vocabulary words utilizing specific types of clues. Strategies for using reference tools, such as a dictionary or glossary, to determine the meaning of an unknown word are also part of direct vocabulary instruction.

Assessing the Three Tiers of Vocabulary Words

In *Bringing Words to Life: Robust Vocabulary Instruction*, Beck, McKeown, and Kucan (2002) concluded that "word knowledge is not an all-or-nothing proposition. Words may be known at different levels." This suggests that teachers should not try to find one "surefire" way to teach vocabulary, but should instead utilize many methods of direct instruction. Words found to be most useful for direct instruction include words that add to the understanding of the text, and words that may be difficult to spell, have varied meanings, and use figurative language.

Beck, McKeown, and Kucan conceptualized three tiers of vocabulary words to categorize the range and types of words in the vocabulary of experienced and proficient language users.

Tier of Vocabulary Words	Description	Example Words
Tier One	Basic words	clock, walk, jump, dog
Tier Two	Frequently used words in oral and written communication	merchant, required, tend, benevolent, absurd, coincidence
Tier Three	Infrequently used words in academic/content discipline subjects and topics	peninsula, refinery, genome, numerator

Tier Two words are often found useful for teaching to students because of their frequency, utility, instructional potential, and general conceptual understanding. These words give students a more precise and sophisticated means of expressing their ideas as they move away from common, redundant, and basic language forms. Although these types of words are valuable, they typically do not focus on the vocabulary from academic subject areas (Marzano, 2003). In 1986, Stahl and Fairbanks conducted a study that cites instruction in Tier Two words yields enhanced content comprehension scores of only 12%. However, when words were selected for instruction based on their critical necessity to understanding academic content, the effect was a 33% increase in content-area comprehension. This research confirms that instruction in content-area words is valuable and necessary for students to internalize academic content.

Benchmark Education resources provide direct vocabulary instruction at all tiers. The assessments in this book enable teachers to evaluate students' vocabulary knowledge throughout the year.

The two-part Tier One assessment provided in this section enables you to evaluate students' reading and spelling of high-frequency words along a developmental continuum. Use the instructions provided below to administer each part of the assessment.

Administering Part One: Reading

- There are six word lists in this assessment, representing the 500 most common words in English, ranked in frequency order. Provide students with a copy of the word list you would like them to read (pp. 14–24).

- Instruct the student to read the words as quickly as possible. Place a checkmark next to each word read instantly and correctly. If the student pauses for three seconds or more, have him/her skip to the next word.

- Use the group High-Frequency Word Assessment class recording forms (pp. 25–30) to document students' assessment results.

Administering Part Two: Spelling

- Distribute the blank High-Frequency Word Spelling Assessment form to students (p. 31).

- Read the list of high-frequency words you would like students to spell (pp. 32–51).

- Collect students' completed assessment and check their answers.

- Use the Group High-Frequency Word Assessment class recording forms to document students' assessment results.

Use the results of these assessments to help you plan future Tier One high-frequency word instruction.

Word List A #1–#25

the	of	and	a	to
in	is	you	that	it
he	was	for	on	are
as	with	his	they	I
at	be	this	have	from

Word List B #26–#65

or	one	had	by	word
but	not	what	all	were
we	when	your	can	said
there	use	an	each	which
she	do	how	their	if
will	up	other	about	out
many	then	them	these	so
some	her	would	make	like

Word List B #66–#100

him	into	time	has	look
two	more	write	go	see
number	no	way	could	people
my	than	first	water	been
call	who	oil	now	find
long	down	day	did	get
come	made	may	part	over

Informal Assessments for Vocabulary Development   ©2011 Benchmark Education Company, LLC

Word List C #101–#150

new	sound	take	only	little
work	know	place	year	live
me	back	give	most	very
after	thing	our	just	name
good	sentence	man	think	say
great	where	help	through	much
before	line	right	too	mean
old	any	same	tell	boy
follow	came	want	show	also
around	form	three	small	set

Word List C #151–#200

put	end	does	another	well
large	must	big	even	such
because	turn	here	why	ask
went	men	read	need	land
different	home	us	move	try
kind	hand	picture	again	change
off	play	spell	air	away
animal	house	point	page	letter
mother	answer	found	study	still
learn	should	America	world	high

Word List D #201–#250

every	near	add	food	between
own	below	country	plant	last
school	father	keep	tree	never
start	city	earth	eye	light
thought	head	under	story	saw
left	don't	few	while	along
might	close	something	seem	next
hard	open	example	begin	life
always	those	both	paper	together
got	group	often	run	important

Word List D #251–#300

until	children	side	feet	car
mile	night	walk	white	sea
began	grow	took	river	four
carry	state	once	book	hear
stop	without	second	late	miss
idea	enough	eat	face	watch
far	Indian	real	almost	let
above	girl	sometimes	mountain	cut
young	talk	soon	list	song
being	leave	family	it's	afternoon

Informal Assessments for Vocabulary Development ©2011 Benchmark Education Company, LLC

Word List E #301–#350

body	music	color	stand	sun
question	fish	area	mark	dog
horse	birds	problem	complete	room
knew	since	ever	piece	told
usually	didn't	friends	easy	heard
order	red	door	sure	become
top	ship	across	today	during
short	better	best	however	low
hours	black	products	happened	whole
measure	remember	early	waves	reached

Word List E #351–#400

listen	wind	rock	space	covered
fast	several	hold	himself	toward
five	step	morning	passed	vowel
true	hundred	against	pattern	numeral
table	north	slowly	money	map
farm	pulled	draw	voice	seen
cold	cried	plan	notice	south
sing	war	ground	fall	king
town	I'll	unit	figure	certain
field	travel	wood	fire	upon

Word List F #401–#450

done	English	road	halt	ten
fly	gave	box	finally	wait
correct	oh	quickly	person	became
shown	minutes	strong	verb	stars
front	feel	fact	inches	street
decided	contain	course	surface	produce
building	ocean	class	note	nothing
rest	carefully	scientists	inside	wheels
stay	green	known	island	week
less	machine	base	ago	stood

Word List F #451–#500

plane	system	behind	ran	round
boat	game	force	brought	understand
warm	common	bring	explain	dry
though	language	shape	deep	thousands
yes	clear	equation	yet	government
filled	heat	full	hot	check
object	am	rule	among	noun
power	cannot	able	six	size
dark	ball	material	special	heavy
fine	pair	circle	include	built

High-Frequency Word Assessment Part One: Reading

Name: _____ Date: _____

Total Number of Words Attempted: _____ Total Number of Words Read Accurately: _____

Chart Coding Legend:
√ accurate reading of word
(teacher's phonetic spelling) inaccurate attempt by child
– no response given

Word List A #1–#25

the	of	and	a	to
in	is	you	that	it
he	was	for	on	are
as	with	his	they	I
at	be	this	have	from

High-Frequency Word Assessment Part One: Reading

Name: _____   Date: _____

Total Number of Words Attempted: _____   Total Number of Words Read Accurately:_____

Chart Coding Legend:
√ accurate reading of word
(teacher's phonetic spelling) inaccurate attempt by child
— no response given

Word List B #26–#100

or	one	had	by	word
but	not	what	all	were
we	when	your	can	said
there	use	an	each	which
she	do	how	their	if
will	up	other	about	out
many	then	them	these	so
some	her	would	make	like
him	into	time	has	look
two	more	write	go	see
number	no	way	could	people
my	than	first	water	been
call	who	oil	now	find
long	down	day	did	get
come	made	may	part	over

Informal Assessments for Vocabulary Development   ©2011 Benchmark Education Company, LLC

High-Frequency Word Assessment Part One: Reading

Name: _____ Date: _____

Total Number of Words Attempted: _____ Total Number of Words Read Accurately: _____

Chart Coding Legend:
√ accurate reading of word
(teacher's phonetic spelling) inaccurate attempt by child
– no response given

Word List C #101–#200

new	sound	take	only	little
work	know	place	year	live
me	back	give	most	very
after	thing	our	just	name
good	sentence	man	think	say
great	where	help	through	much
before	line	right	too	mean
old	any	same	tell	boy
follow	came	want	show	also
around	form	three	small	set
put	end	does	another	well
large	must	big	even	such
because	turn	here	why	ask
went	men	read	need	land
different	home	us	move	try
kind	hand	picture	again	change
off	play	spell	air	away
animal	house	point	page	letter
mother	answer	found	study	still
learn	should	America	world	high

High-Frequency Word Assessment Part One: Reading

Name: _____   Date: _____

Total Number of Words Attempted: _____   Total Number of Words Read Accurately: _____

Chart Coding Legend:
√ accurate reading of word
(teacher's phonetic spelling) inaccurate attempt by child
– no response given

Word List D #201–#300

every	near	add	food	between
own	below	country	plant	last
school	father	keep	tree	never
start	city	earth	eye	light
thought	head	under	story	saw
left	don't	few	while	along
might	close	something	seem	next
hard	open	example	begin	life
always	those	both	paper	together
got	group	often	run	important
until	children	side	feet	car
mile	night	walk	white	sea
began	grow	took	river	four
carry	state	once	book	hear
stop	without	second	late	miss
idea	enough	eat	face	watch
far	Indian	real	almost	let
above	girl	sometimes	mountain	cut
young	talk	soon	list	song
being	leave	family	it's	afternoon

High-Frequency Word Assessment Part One: Reading

Name: _____ Date: _____

Total Number of Words Attempted: _____ Total Number of Words Read Accurately: _____

Chart Coding Legend:
√ accurate reading of word
(teacher's phonetic spelling) inaccurate attempt by child
– no response given

Word List E #301–#400

body	music	color	stand	sun
question	fish	area	mark	dog
horse	birds	problem	complete	room
knew	since	ever	piece	told
usually	didn't	friends	easy	heard
order	red	door	sure	become
top	ship	across	today	during
short	better	best	however	low
hours	black	products	happened	whole
measure	remember	early	waves	reached
listen	wind	rock	space	covered
fast	several	hold	himself	toward
five	step	morning	passed	vowel
true	hundred	against	pattern	numeral
table	north	slowly	money	map
farm	pulled	draw	voice	seen
cold	cried	plan	notice	south
sing	war	ground	fall	king
town	I'll	unit	figure	certain
field	travel	wood	fire	upon

High-Frequency Word Assessment Part One: Reading

Name: _____ Date: _____

Total Number of Words Attempted: _____ Total Number of Words Read Accurately:_____

Chart Coding Legend:
√ accurate reading of word
(teacher's phonetic spelling) inaccurate attempt by child
– no response given

Word List F #401–#500

done	English	road	halt	ten
fly	gave	box	finally	wait
correct	oh	quickly	person	became
shown	minutes	strong	verb	stars
front	feel	fact	inches	street
decided	contain	course	surface	produce
building	ocean	class	note	nothing
rest	carefully	scientists	inside	wheels
stay	green	known	island	week
less	machine	base	ago	stood
plane	system	behind	ran	round
boat	game	force	brought	understand
warm	common	bring	explain	dry
though	language	shape	deep	thousands
yes	clear	equation	yet	government
filled	heat	full	hot	check
object	am	rule	among	noun
power	cannot	able	six	size
dark	ball	material	special	heavy
fine	pair	circle	include	built

High-Frequency Word Assessment Part Two: Spelling

Name: _____ Date: _____

Word List: _____

Group High-Frequency Word Assessment

Chart Coding Legend:
(√) words read and spelled correctly
(x) words read correctly but not spelled correctly
(-) words not attempted/no response

List A #1–#25

Student's Name

Date: _____

the													
of													
and													
a													
to													
in													
is													
you													
that													
it													
he													
was													
for													
on													
are													
as													
with													
his													
they													
I													
at													
be													
this													
have													
from													

Group High-Frequency Word Assessment

Chart Coding Legend:
(√) words read and spelled correctly
(x) words read correctly but not spelled correctly
(-) words not attempted/no response

List B #26–#50

Date: _____

Student's Name												
or												
one												
had												
by												
word												
but												
not												
what												
all												
were												
we												
when												
your												
can												
said												
there												
use												
an												
each												
which												
she												
do												
how												
their												
if												

Group High-Frequency Word Assessment

Chart Coding Legend:
(√) words read and spelled correctly
(x) words read correctly but not spelled correctly
(-) words not attempted/no response

List B #51–#75

Student's Name

Date: _____

will													
up													
other													
about													
out													
many													
then													
them													
these													
so													
some													
her													
would													
make													
like													
him													
into													
time													
has													
look													
two													
more													
write													
go													
see													

Informal Assessments for Vocabulary Development

Group High-Frequency Word Assessment

Chart Coding Legend:
(√) words read and spelled correctly
(x) words read correctly but not spelled correctly
(-) words not attempted/no response

List B #76–#100

Student's Name

Date: _____

number													
no													
way													
could													
people													
my													
than													
first													
water													
been													
call													
who													
oil													
now													
find													
long													
down													
day													
did													
get													
come													
made													
may													
part													
over													

Group High-Frequency Word Assessment

Chart Coding Legend:
(√) words read and spelled correctly
(x) words read correctly but not spelled correctly
(-) words not attempted/no response

List C #101–#125

Date: _____

Student's Name													
new													
sound													
take													
only													
little													
work													
know													
place													
year													
live													
me													
back													
give													
most													
very													
after													
thing													
our													
just													
name													
good													
sentence													
man													
think													
say													

Informal Assessments for Vocabulary Development

Group High-Frequency Word Assessment

List C #126–#150

Student's Name

Date: _____

great											
where											
help											
through											
much											
before											
line											
right											
too											
mean											
old											
any											
same											
tell											
boy											
follow											
came											
want											
show											
also											
around											
form											
three											
small											
set											

Group High-Frequency Word Assessment

Chart Coding Legend:
(√) words read and spelled correctly
(x) words read correctly but not spelled correctly
(-) words not attempted/no response

List C #151–#175

Student's Name

Date: _____

put												
end												
does												
another												
well												
large												
must												
big												
even												
such												
because												
turn												
here												
why												
ask												
went												
men												
read												
need												
land												
different												
home												
us												
move												
try												

Group High-Frequency Word Assessment

Chart Coding Legend:
(√) words read and spelled correctly
(x) words read correctly but not spelled correctly
(-) words not attempted/no response

List C #176–#200

Student's Name

Date: _____

kind												
hand												
picture												
again												
change												
off												
play												
spell												
air												
away												
animal												
house												
point												
page												
letter												
mother												
answer												
found												
study												
still												
learn												
should												
America												
world												
high												

Group High-Frequency Word Assessment

Chart Coding Legend:
(√) words read and spelled correctly
(x) words read correctly but not spelled correctly
(-) words not attempted/no response

List D #201–#225

Student's Name

Date: _____

every													
near													
add													
food													
between													
own													
below													
country													
plant													
last													
school													
father													
keep													
tree													
never													
start													
city													
earth													
eye													
light													
thought													
head													
under													
story													
saw													

Group High-Frequency Word Assessment

Chart Coding Legend:
(√) words read and spelled correctly
(x) words read correctly but not spelled correctly
(-) words not attempted/no response

List D #226–#250

Date: _____

Student's Name												
left												
don't												
few												
while												
along												
might												
close												
something												
seem												
next												
hard												
open												
example												
begin												
life												
always												
those												
both												
paper												
together												
got												
group												
often												
run												
important												

Group High-Frequency Word Assessment

Chart Coding Legend:
(√) words read and spelled correctly
(x) words read correctly but not spelled correctly
(-) words not attempted/no response

List D #251–#275

Date: _____

	Student's Name											
until												
children												
side												
feet												
car												
mile												
night												
walk												
white												
sea												
began												
grow												
took												
river												
four												
carry												
state												
once												
book												
hear												
stop												
without												
second												
late												
miss												

Group High-Frequency Word Assessment

Chart Coding Legend:
(√) words read and spelled correctly
(x) words read correctly but not spelled correctly
(-) words not attempted/no response

List D #276–#300

Student's Name

Date: _____

idea												
enough												
eat												
face												
watch												
far												
Indian												
real												
almost												
let												
above												
girl												
sometimes												
mountain												
cut												
young												
talk												
soon												
list												
song												
being												
leave												
family												
it's												
afternoon												

Group High-Frequency Word Assessment

Chart Coding Legend:
(√) words read and spelled correctly
(x) words read correctly but not spelled correctly
(-) words not attempted/no response

List E #301–#325

Student's Name

Date: _____

body														
music														
color														
stand														
sun														
question														
fish														
area														
mark														
dog														
horse														
birds														
problem														
complete														
room														
knew														
since														
ever														
piece														
told														
usually														
didn't														
friends														
easy														
heard														

Group High-Frequency Word Assessment

Chart Coding Legend:
(√) words read and spelled correctly
(x) words read correctly but not spelled correctly
(-) words not attempted/no response

List E #326–#350

Student's Name

Date: _____

order												
red												
door												
sure												
become												
top												
ship												
across												
today												
during												
short												
better												
best												
however												
low												
hours												
black												
products												
happened												
whole												
measure												
remember												
early												
waves												
reached												

Group High-Frequency Word Assessment

Chart Coding Legend:
(√) words read and spelled correctly
(x) words read correctly but not spelled correctly
(-) words not attempted/no response

List E #351–#375

Student's Name

Date: _____

listen													
wind													
rock													
space													
covered													
fast													
several													
hold													
himself													
toward													
five													
step													
morning													
passed													
vowel													
true													
hundred													
against													
pattern													
numeral													
table													
north													
slowly													
money													
map													

Group High-Frequency Word Assessment

Chart Coding Legend:
(√) words read and spelled correctly
(x) words read correctly but not spelled correctly
(-) words not attempted/no response

List E #376–#400

Date: _____

Student's Name												
farm												
pulled												
draw												
voice												
seen												
cold												
cried												
plan												
notice												
south												
sing												
war												
ground												
fall												
king												
town												
I'll												
unit												
figure												
certain												
field												
travel												
wood												
fire												
upon												

Group High-Frequency Word Assessment

Chart Coding Legend:
(√) words read and spelled correctly
(x) words read correctly but not spelled correctly
(-) words not attempted/no response

List F #401–#425

Student's Name

Date: _____

done													
English													
road													
halt													
ten													
fly													
gave													
box													
finally													
wait													
correct													
oh													
quickly													
person													
became													
shown													
minutes													
strong													
verb													
stars													
front													
feel													
fact													
inches													
street													

Informal Assessments for Vocabulary Development

Group High-Frequency Word Assessment

Chart Coding Legend:
(√) words read and spelled correctly
(x) words read correctly but not spelled correctly
(-) words not attempted/no response

List F #426–#450

Date: _____

Student's Name												
decided												
contain												
course												
surface												
produce												
building												
ocean												
class												
note												
nothing												
rest												
carefully												
scientists												
inside												
wheels												
stay												
green												
known												
island												
week												
less												
machine												
base												
ago												
stood												

Group High-Frequency Word Assessment

Chart Coding Legend:
(√) words read and spelled correctly
(x) words read correctly but not spelled correctly
(-) words not attempted/no response

List F #451–#475

Student's Name

Date: _____

plane											
system											
behind											
ran											
round											
boat											
game											
force											
brought											
understand											
warm											
common											
bring											
explain											
dry											
though											
language											
shape											
deep											
thousands											
yes											
clear											
equation											
yet											
government											

Group High-Frequency Word Assessment

Chart Coding Legend:
(√) words read and spelled correctly
(x) words read correctly but not spelled correctly
(-) words not attempted/no response

List F #476–#500

Date: _____

Student's Name												
filled												
heat												
full												
hot												
check												
object												
am												
rule												
among												
noun												
power												
cannot												
able												
six												
size												
dark												
ball												
material												
special												
heavy												
fine												
pair												
circle												
include												
built												

"The assessment of vocabulary instruction should be varied and meaningful. Students need ways to ascertain both their ability to determine the meaning of an unfamiliar word and to demonstrate the knowledge of words at the heart of an instructional unit."

—Allen, 1999

Assessment is a critical component of all instruction. Traditional tests do not give a true picture of vocabulary acquisition. Instead, assessments should focus on ensuring students are on the road to becoming independent word learners (Baker, Simmons, Kame'enui, 1995).

The pages that follow offer a range of informal assessments that can show teachers a great deal about the level to which their students have internalized the focus vocabulary. Knowledge rating blackline masters provide students with an opportunity to honestly assess their own understanding of the target vocabulary words. Students are asked to place a check mark under the appropriate column that reflects their current understanding of each term.

Vocabulary notebooks provide students an optimal place to record their thoughts about new words and serve as a valid record of authentic learning. These notebooks can become a treasured resource and assessment piece.

These tools, in conjunction with the vocabulary graphic organizers, help teachers develop and evaluate students' knowledge of Tier Two and Tier Three vocabulary. Students are able to demonstrate what they already know about words, and they are encouraged to compare and contrast, categorize, and analyze word parts to extend their knowledge.

Graphic Organizer	Tier Two Vocabulary	Tier Three Vocabulary
Key Terms Self-Assessment	√	√
Vocabulary Notebook	√	√
Concept Circle	√	√
Semantic Feature Analysis		√
Pedestal Word Chart		√
Compare and Contrast	√	√
Venn Diagram	√	√
Word Map	√	√
List-Group-Label		√
Sensory Experience Chart	√	√
Etymology	√	√
Closed Compound Words	√	√
Open Compound Words	√	√
Suffixes	√	√
Homophones	√	√
Multiple Meanings	√	√

Name _____ Date _____

Key Terms Self-Assessment

How well do you know these words? Place a ✓ in the appropriate column for each term.

Key Term	I Know the Word	I Think I Know the Word	I Do Not Know the Word
climate			
clouds			
condensation			
evaporation			
precipitation			
storms			
temperature			
water cycle			
water vapor			
weather			

How has your understanding of these words changed? Place a ✓ in the appropriate column for each term.

Key Term	I Know the Word	I Think I Know the Word	I Do Not Know the Word
climate			
clouds			
condensation			
evaporation			
precipitation			
storms			
temperature			
water cycle			
water vapor			
weather			

Vocabulary Notebook

1. Show what you know about water. Write a definition or sentence, or draw a picture in the space below.	**2.** Show what you know about the water cycle. Write a definition or sentence, or draw a picture in the space below.
3. Show what you know about weather. Write a definition or sentence, or draw a picture in the space below.	**4.** Show what you know about storms. Write a definition or sentence, or draw a picture in the space below.

5. Write a definition for the term **climate**.

Concept Circle

Directions: Complete each section of the circle. Write at least two facts that explain _____ , _____ , and _____ .

Theme

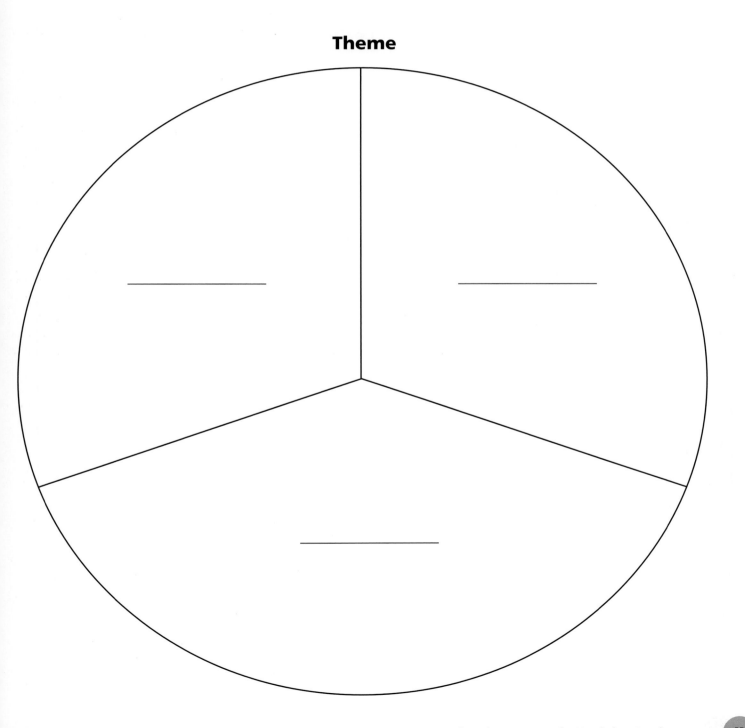

Semantic Feature Analysis

Directions: Place an X in the column that best describes the [feature being addressed] each category name has. Then state your conclusion at the bottom of the page.

Category:	Feature:	Feature:	Feature:
Example:			
Example:			
Example:			
Example:			

I conclude _____

_____ .

Name _____ Date _____

Pedestal Word Chart

Directions: Record facts, descriptions, or phrases to show what you
know about _____ . Write your responses in
the chart below.

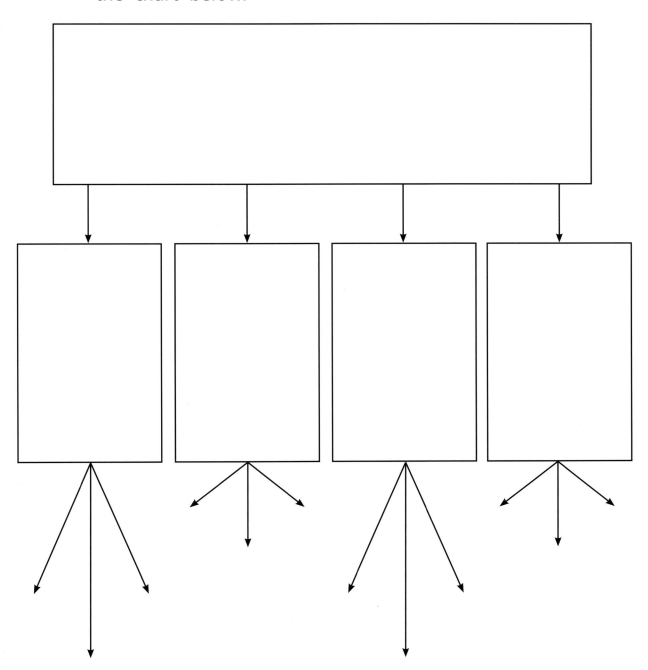

Name _____ Date _____

Compare and Contrast

Directions: Use the chart below to compare and contrast words or phrases. Then write a conclusion statement on the line.

Connection Between the _____ and _____	Distinguishing Feature	Characteristics
_____		
_____		

Conclusion Statement _____

Venn Diagram

Directions: Use the Venn diagram to identify how _____ and _____ are alike and different.

_____ **both** _____

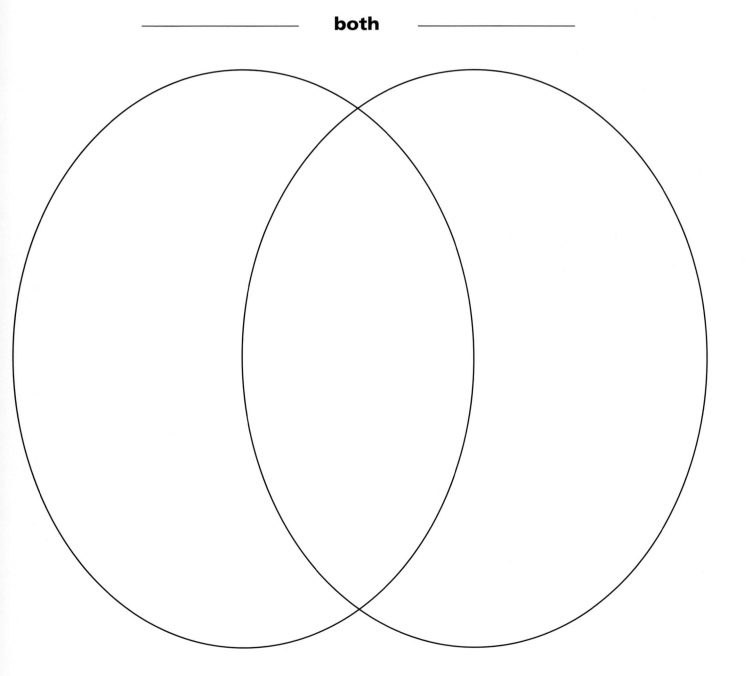

Name _____ Date _____

Word Map

Directions: Use the word map to study the word _____ .
Record a definition, synonym, description, and examples.

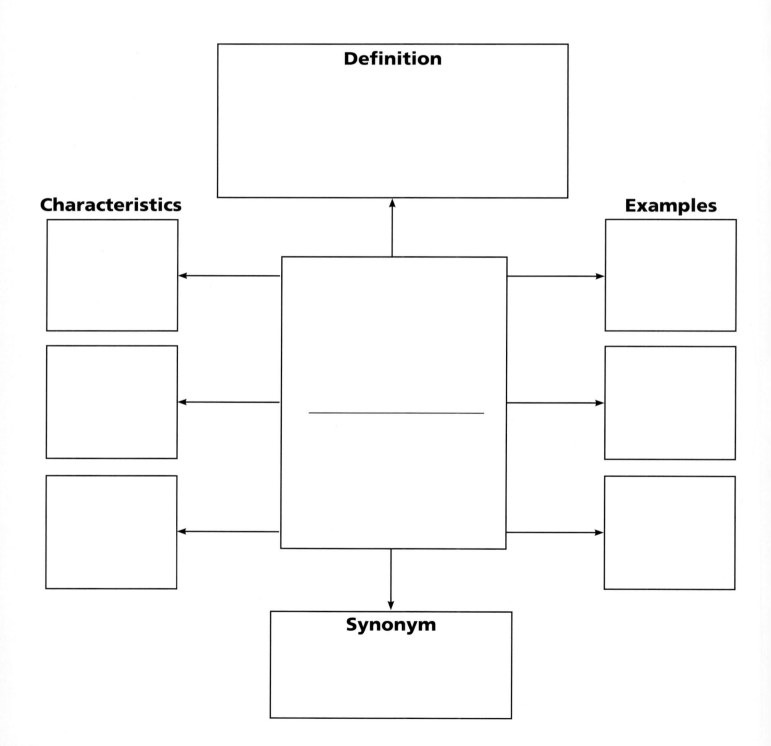

Definition

Characteristics

Examples

_____

Synonym

©2011 Benchmark Education Company, LLC

List-Group-Label

Directions: Think about _____ . In the first column, brainstorm a list of words that relate to the topic. Create groups of related words in the second column. Then, label the groups in the final column.

List	Group	Label

Sensory Experience Chart

Directions: Use your senses to visualize what you know about _____ . Then use the chart below to record what you see, hear, and feel.

Theme:	Sight	Sound	Feelings
Event or Scene: _____			
Event or Scene 2: _____			

Name _____ Date _____

Etymology

Directions: Write a vocabulary word in the first column. Write the word part or parts in the second column. Find the origin and meaning of the word parts. Then use the last column to write what you think the word means.

Word	Word Parts	Origin and Meaning	Possible Definition

Closed Compound Words

Directions: Write closed compound words in the first column. Write the first smaller word in the second column. Write the second smaller word in the third column. Then write a definition of the closed compound word.

Closed Compound Word	Word #1	Word #2	Closed Compound Word Definition

Name _____ Date _____

Open Compound Words

Directions: Write open compound words in the first column. Write the first smaller word in the second column. Write the second smaller word in the third column. Then write a definition of the open compound word.

Open Compound Word	Word #1	Word #2	Open Compound Word Definition

Suffixes

Directions: As you read the text, find words with the suffix
_____ . Write each word in the first column.
Write the base word in the second column. Write the suffix
of the word in the third column. Then write the definition
in the last column.

Word	Base Word	Suffix	Definition

Name _____ Date _____

Homophones

Directions: Think of words that have the same sound but are spelled differently and have different meanings. Write those words in the first column. Write the definition of each word in the second column. Write where you might see this word in the third column. Then write a sentence using the word in the last column.

Homophone	Definition	Where I Might See This Word	Example Sentence

Multiple Meanings

Directions: Write a vocabulary word in each center oval. Then write three definitions for each word in the boxes provided. You may use a dictionary, thesaurus, books, or other resources to help you find definitions.

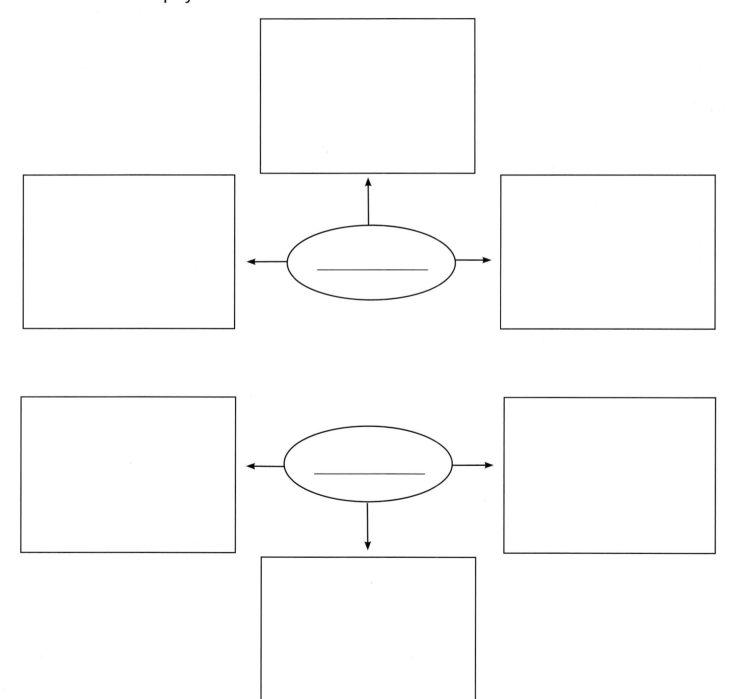

Vocabulary understandings can be examined by individual word meaning, and a variety of word solving strategies that readers use to maintain comprehension. It is important to note how students are acquiring vocabulary across all three tiers and how they are linking prior knowledge to new contexts while listening, speaking, reading and writing.

The wide variety of assessment tools in this book provides teachers with many examples to examine degree of word knowledge and application of vocabulary strategy development. When discussing vocabulary development, also consider the developmental stages of reading development and the demands of texts that readers are encountering over time. Reference the developmental characteristics of readers over time found in *Informal Assessments for Reading Development* on pages 12 to 31 to analyze reading behaviors and characteristics at various stages of development. In addition, as you reflect on key developmental characteristics and how readers interact with instructional level texts, also take into account their metacognitive, vocabulary, and word-solving strategy understandings.

As you observe students reading, ask yourself the following questions to guide your ongoing assessment of vocabulary development.

Do the substitutions students make for challenging words while reading maintain the meaning of the text? Do their substitutions cause a breakdown of comprehension? Are students aware when their miscues do not maintain the meaning of the text?

Are students able to read Tier One (frequently found words) fluently without having to stop and decode these types of words? Are students showing control of a growing number of core, high-frequency and sight words as readers and writers?

Are students transferring content knowledge and vocabulary while reading nonfiction texts? Are they making links to prior learning and current units of study in the content areas?

Are students showing flexibility in the use of multiple meaning words? Are they choosing appropriate word meanings to support comprehension before/during/ after reading?

When assessing vocabulary understanding, Dougherty Stahl & Bravo (2010) remind us that word knowledge is a matter of degree and can grow over time. Incremental knowledge of a word occurs with multiple exposures in meaningful contexts. While observing students during discussions, reading, or writing, note how their vocabulary understandings across all three tiers are developing.

Tier One Words: Are students increasing their control over high-frequency and sight words? Does their reading development growth reflect a growing sight and writing vocabulary? (see also Cunningham and Fry word lists)

Tier Two Words: Are students applying new understandings of words across multiple contexts? Are students making connections, linking and building word associations and categories of meaning? Are students able to describe, define, and use rich language and word understandings? (see also Beck, McKeown, & Kucan)

Tier Three Words: Are students gaining academic vocabulary and using word meaning and terms correctly in content area, nonfiction texts? (see also Marzano's list of academic vocabulary)

Bravo and Cervetti (2008) remind us that academic vocabulary (Tier Three words) understandings range from having no control of a word (where students have never seen or heard the word) to passive control on the continuum (where students can decode the term and provide a synonym or basic definition) and active control (where students can decode the word, provide a definition, situate it in connection to other words in the discipline, and use it in their oral and written communications).

Cronbach's dimensions of vocabulary and word knowledge include the following:

- Generalization (the ability to define a word)
- Application (selecting an appropriate use of the word)
- Breadth (knowledge of multiple meanings of the word)
- Precision (the ability to apply a term correctly to all situations)
- Availability (the ability to use the word productively)
- Receptive/Productive (words understood when they are read or heard and then used correctly when talking or writing)

While observing and assessing students, look for evidence of vocabulary knowledge and transfer during discussions and in their writing. In addition to the wide variety of vocabulary assessment tools in this handbook, additional ways to assess vocabulary include the following.

- Asking questions (orally or in writing; multiple choice, constructed response, fill in the blank)
- Matching words to definitions
- CLOZE passages (sentence, paragraph, or passage fill in the blank)
- Generating a sentence with targeted words (oral or written)
- Retellings
- Providing synonyms, antonyms, descriptions, examples and definitions
- Identifying word structure and meanings of word parts
- Creating categories and groupings of words
- Completing or creating analogies
- One-minute brainstorming quick write lists
- Comparing and contrasting
- Oral or artistic representations of word meaning and related groups of terms
- Graphic organizers
- Rubrics and checklists
- Self-evaluation tasks

When evaluating students' responses and answers to questions related to word meaning and word solving strategy understandings, consider where their strengths and needs are and ways to build and support vocabulary development. Use the following questions to guide your thinking and observations of students before/during/after reading.

Are students aware when comprehension breaks down due to lack of vocabulary understandings? What strategies do they use to fix and repair comprehension?

Do students use strategies flexibly and make associations and links to other words, categories, and grammatical structures?

Do students decode words fluently and accurately? Are they using a variety of decoding and problem solving strategies to read challenging words, such as using sound, visual, and syllable patterns?

Are students using what they know about affixes (prefixes, suffixes), root words and base words, word origin to aid in determining word meaning and maintaining comprehension?

Do students use context clues (synonyms, antonyms, direct definitions, descriptions, examples) to unlock the meaning of unknown or challenging words?

Do students use text elements, text features, and graphic aids to enhance vocabulary understandings?

Do students apply understandings in new or different contexts?

Do you see evidence of transfer of new understandings in students' writing, discussions, and comprehension of other texts or contexts?

When faced with a word solving issue that they are unable to solve independently, do they seek help from a resource or others?

Individual Reading Conference

Student Name: _____ Date: _____

Book Title: _____ Author: _____ Pages: ____ to ____

Part One: Independent Reading Recap

Why did you choose this book? What are you interested in reading about? Do you need help finding a new book?

How is the difficulty of the text for you? How do you know?

Summarize or retell what has been happening (or what you have learned) so far.

Tell me what you remember most about what you've read.

Notes: _____

_____

Part Two: Vocabulary Connections

What new words have you encountered in your reading?

What strategies did you use to figure out the meaning of these words? Did you use context clues? Did you look at the word parts for clues? Tell me about your thinking.

What words that you've learned would you like to incorporate into your own writing? Explain.

The next time you come across an unfamiliar word in a text you are reading, what are three things you can do to help yourself figure out that word?

Notes: _____

_____

Part Three: Oral Reading Record

Conduct an oral reading record on the independent reading selection or from a text read previously in small group Guided Reading lessons.

Attach the oral reading record form to your Individual Reading Conference note-taking form when finished.

Record notes for observations and next steps instructionally below.

Notes: _____

_____

Part Four: Action Planning

What are your strengths/needs/goals as a reader? How can I help you achieve them?

When do you anticipate finishing this book?

What is next on your list of must-read titles?

Notes: _____

_____

Prompting to Support Vocabulary Development

As an observant and responsive teacher, having a variety of prompting stems for a variety of purposes is a valuable resource. Each category of prompts promotes a distinct strategy for solving words.

Strategies for Solving Words*	Prompts
By Metacognitive Awareness for Fix-Up and Monitoring Notice errors and fix them while reading or writing	Which word was tricky for you? Where's the tricky part? Show me the word(s) that were challenging for you. You noticed what was wrong. Find the part that's not quite right. There's a tricky word on this line. What did you notice? What's wrong? Why did you stop? Something wasn't quite right. You made a mistake. Can you find it? You almost got that. See if you can find what is wrong. Try it. Try that again. Try it another way. What could you try? What do you know that might help? Were you right? Think about what would make sense. Think about what would sound right. That makes sense, but does it look right? That sounds right, but does it look right?
By Sound (Phonemic Strategies) Read or write words by thinking about the sounds	It starts like ___. It ends like ___. It starts like that. Now check the last part. What would you expect to see at the beginning [or end]? Try the first part. You've got the first part [or last part] right. Try decoding the word by syllables. Use what you know about letter clusters and syllable patterns to decode the part that is challenging for you. Look at the syllables; what sound will the vowel make? Try it; does that sound right? Now try a different vowel sound.

Strategies for Solving Words*	Prompts
By Look (Visual Strategies) Read or write words by thinking about the way they look.	Look at the parts. Get a good look at the word. Do you think it looks like ___ (word)? Think about how the word looks. Do you see smaller words within the big word?
By Meaning (Morphemic Strategies) Read or write words by thinking about what they mean.	Do you see a part that you know? Do you see a part that can help you? What is the base word? What does it mean? Is there an inflectional ending? What does it mean? What is the prefix? What does that mean? What is the suffix? What does that mean? Is there a Greek or Latin element in the word? What does it mean? What part of speech is the word? What would the word mean?
By Connections (Linking Strategies) Use what you know about a word to figure out a new word.	Do you know a word like that? Do you know a word that ends with those letters? What other word do you know like that?
By Inquiry (Research Strategies) Use reference materials to learn more about words.	Try three other ways to solve your problem before you check a source or ask me for help. Try looking up the word in a dictionary or thesaurus. Have you seen this word in a text before? Find it and think about what it means. Ask a friend if he or she knows what the word means.

*Adapted from Fountas & Pinnell. Pages 370, 383 *Guiding Readers and Writers*

Year-at-a-Glance Planning Calendar

Teacher Name: _____   Grade: _____   Level: _____

Notes:	August	September	October
November	**December**	**January**	**February**
March	**April**	**May**	**June**

Month-at-a-Glance Planning Calendar

Teacher Name: _____ Grade: _____ Level: _____

	Monday	Tuesday	Wednesday	Thursday	Friday
Week of:					
Week of:					
Week of:					
Week of:					

Informal Assessments for Vocabulary Development

Week-at-a-Glance Planning Calendar

Teacher Name: _____   Grade: _____   Level: _____

	Monday	Tuesday	Wednesday	Thursday	Friday
Progress-Monitoring Assessments					
Individual Reading Conferences					

Anecdotal Notes

Teacher Name: _____   Grade: _____   Level: _____

Informal Assessments for Vocabulary Development

BIBLIOGRAPHY

Allen, Janet. (1999). *Words, words, words: Teaching vocabulary in grades 4–12.* York, ME: Stenhouse Publisher

Anderson, R.C., & Freebody, P. (1981). Vocabulary knowledge. In J.T. Guthrie (Ed.), *Comprehension and Teaching: Research reviews* (pp. 77–117). Newark, DE: International Reading Association.

Anderson, R.C., & Freebody, P. (1983). Reading comprehension and the assessment and acquisition of word knowledge. InB. Hutson (Ed.), *Advances in reading/language research* (pp. 231–256). Greenwich, CT: JAI.

Anderson, R.C., & Freebody, P. (1985). Vocabulary knowledge. In H. Singer & R.B. Ruddell (Eds.), *Theoretical models and processes of reading* (3rd ed., pp. 343–371). Newark, DE:International Reading Association.

Baker, S., Kame'enui, E.K., & Simmons, D. (1995). "Vocabulary Acquisition: Synthesis of the Research." National Center to Improve the Tools of Educators.

Beck, I.L., McKeown, M.G., & Kucan, L. (2002). *Bringing words to life: Robust vocabulary instruction.* New York: Guilford.

Beck, I.L., McKeown, M.G., & Omanson, R.C. (1987). The effects and uses of diverse vocabulary instructional techniques. In M.G. McKeown & M.E. Curtis (Eds.), *The nature of vocabulary acquisition* (pp. 147–163). Hillsdale, NJ: Erlbaum.

Blachowicz, C.L.Z., & Fisher, P.J. (2006). *Teaching vocabulary in all classrooms* (3rd ed.). Upper Saddle River, NJ: Pearson Education.

Bravo, M.A., & Cervetti, G.N. (2008). Teaching vocabulary through text and experience in content areas. In A.E. Farstrup & S.J. Samuels (Eds.), *What research has to say about vocabulary instruction* (pp. 130–149). Newark, DE: International Reading Association.

Bravo, M.A., Cervetti, G.N., Hiebert, E.H., & Pearson, P.D. (2008). *From passive to active control of science vocabulary* (56th yearbook of the National Reading Conference, pp. 122–135). Chicago: National Reading Conference.

Calfee, R.C., & Drum, P. (1986). Research on teaching reading. In M. Wittrock (Ed.), *Handbook of research on teaching* (pp. 804–849). New York: Macmillan.

Cronbach, L.J. (1942). Measuring knowledge of precise word meaning. *The Journal of Educational Research*, 36(7), 528–534.

Dale, E. (1965). Vocabulary measurement: Techniques and major findings. *Elementary English*, 42(8), 895–901.

Dougherty Stahl, K.A., & Bravo, M.A. "Contemporary classroom vocabulary assessment for content areas." *The Reading Teacher,* 2010, 63(7), 566–478, IRA.

Johnson, D.D., Moe, A.J., & Baumann, J.F. (1983). *The Ginn word book for teachers: A basic lexicon.* Boston: Ginn.

Johnson, D.D., & Pearson, P.D. (1984). *Teaching reading vocabulary.* New York: Holt, Rinehart and Winston.

Marzano, R. J., and Pickering, D. J. (2005). *Building Academic Vocabulary: Teacher's Manual*. Alexandria, VA: Association for Supervision and Curriculum Development.

Nagy, W.E., & Scott, J.A. (2000). Vocabulary Processing. In M.L. Kamil, P.B. Mosenthal, P.D. Pearson, & R. Barr (Eds.), *Handbook of reading research* (Vol. 3, pp. 269–274). Mahwah, NJ: Erlbaum.

National Assessment Governing Board. (2009). *Reading framework for the 2009 National Assessment of Educational Progress*. Retrieved December 29, 2009, from www.nagb.org/ publications/frameworks/reading09.pdf

National Clearinghouse for English Language Acquisition. (2007). National Clearinghouse for English Language Acquisition Report: NCELA frequently asked questions. Washington, DC: U.S. Department of Education. Retrieved October 2, 2007, from www.ncela.gwu.edu/faqs

National Institute of Child Health and Human Development. (2000). *Report of the National Reading Panel. Teaching children to read: An evidence-based assessment of the scientific research literature on reading and its implications for reading instruction.* (NIH Publication No. 00 4769). Washington, DC: National Institute of Child Health and Human Development.

Paris, S.G. (2005). Reinterpreting the development of reading skills. *Reading Research Quarterly*, 40(2), 184–202. doi:10.1598/RRQ.40.2.3

Qian, D.D. (2002). Investigating the relationship between vocabulary knowledge and academic reading performance: An assessment perspective. *Language Learning*, 52(3), 513–536. doi:10.1111/1467-9922.00193

Read, J. (2000). *Assessing vocabulary*. Cambridge, England: Cambridge University Press.

Rhodes, L.K. & Shanklin, N.L. (1993). *Windows into Literacy: Assessing Learners K–8*. Portsmouth, NH: Heinemann.

Stahl, S.A., & Fairbanks, M.M. The effects of vocabulary instruction: A model-based meta analysis. *Review of Educational Research*, 56(1) (1986): 72–110.

Stahl, K.A.D. (2008). The effects of three instructional methods on the reading comprehension and content acquisition of novice readers. *Journal of Literacy Research*, 40(3), 359–393. doi:10.1080/10862960802520594

Stahl, S.A., & Nagy, W.E. (2006). *Teaching word meanings*. Mahwah, NJ: Erlbaum.

Stahl, S.A., & Stahl, K.A.D. (2004). Word wizards all! Teaching word meanings in preschool and primary education. In J.F. Baumann & E.J. Kame'enui (Eds.), *Vocabulary instruction: Research to practice* (pp. 59–78). New York: Guilford.

Tomlinson, C.A., & McTighe, J. *Integrating Differentiated Instruction and Understanding by Design*. ASCD: 2006

Wesche, M., & Paribakht, T.S. (1996). Assessing second language vocabulary knowledge: Depth versus breadth. *Canadian Modern Language Review*, 53(1), 13–40.